D1101481

The Simpsons™, created by Matt Groening, is the copyrighted
and trademarked property of Twentieth Century Fox Film Corporation.
Used with permission. All rights reserved.

THE SIMPSONS: 2010 ANNUAL

Copyright © 2008 & 2009 Bongo Entertainment, Inc. and Matt Groening Productions, Inc.
All rights reserved. No part of this book may be used or reproduced in any manner whatsoever
without written permission except in the case of brief quotations
embodied in critical articles and reviews.

For information address
Bongo Comics Group
P.O. Box 1963, Santa Monica, CA 90406-1963, USA

Published in the UK by Titan Books, a division of
Titan Publishing Group, 144 Southwark St., London, SE1 0UP,
under licence from Bongo Entertainment, Inc. and Matt Groening Productions, Inc.

This book is sold subject to the condition that it shall not, by way of trade or otherwise,
be lent, resold, hired out or otherwise circulated without the publisher's prior consent in any form of
binding or cover other than that in which it is published and without a similar condition,
including this condition, being imposed upon the subsequent purchaser.

FIRST EDITION: AUGUST 2009

ISBN: 9781848563438

1 3 5 7 9 10 8 6 4 2

Publisher: Matt Groening
Creative Director: Bill Morrison
Managing Editor: Terry Delegeane
Director of Operations: Robert Zaugh
Art Director: Nathan Kane
Art Director Special Projects: Serban Cristescu
Production Manager: Christopher Ungar
Assistant Art Director: Chia-Hsien Jason Ho
Production/Design: Karen Bates, Nathan Hamill, Art Villanueva
Staff Artist: Mike Rote
Administration: Sherri Smith, Pete Benson
Legal Guardian: Susan A. Grode

Trade Paperback Concepts and Design: Serban Cristescu

Cover: Chia-Hsien Jason Ho, Mike Rote and Serban Cristescu

Contributing Artists:
Karen Bates, John Costanza, Mike DeCarlo, Shane Glines, Nathan Hamill, Chia-Hsien Jason Ho,
James Lloyd, Bill Morrison, Kevin M. Newman, Phyllis Novin, Phil Ortiz, Andrew Pepoy, Jeremy Robinson,
Mike Rote, Robert Stanley, Steve Steere Jr., Carlos Valenti
Contributing Writers:
James W. Bates, Paul Dini, Tony DiGerolamo, Arie Kaplan, Misty Lee, Scott Shaw!, Mary Trainor

PRINTED IN ITALY

Jessica Lovejoy says, "Make mine a SQUISHEE!"

Try our NEW hi-protein beef-flavored SQUISHEE.

It's the ooze to choose for Springfield's bright, young, sophisticated set.

KWIK-E-MART

Sold exclusively at KWIK-E-Mart

Video surveillance now in Hi-Def!

MATT GROENING

YES, FLANDERS, THERE IS A SANTA CLAUS

JAMES W. BATES
SCRIPT

JEREMY ROBINSON
PENCILS

SHANE GLINES
INKS

ROBERT STANLEY
COLORS

KAREN BATES
LETTERS

BILL MORRISON
EDITOR

AT LEAST IT DOESN'T SAY *X*-MAS.

MILK

MILK

EGG NOG

EGG NOG

EGG NOG – It's what Christmas is all about!

HAVE A DONUT Make it a Hole-y Night

UGH!

SIR, MAY I INTEREST YOU IN AN X-MAS CONFECTION? I AM ALMOST SOLD OUT OF CHOCOLATE SANTA CLAUSES BUT I DO HAVE PLENTY OF SUGAR BABY JESUSES LEFT!

KWIKE BEEF

I DON'T KNOW WHAT MAKES ME ANGRIER, THAT YOU HAVE CANDY IDOLS OF OUR LORD OR THAT SANTA IS OUT SELLING THEM.

IF *YOU* CAN FORGIVE ME FOR SELLING THE CANDY, I WILL FORGIVE *YOU* FOR MAKING SLOPPY JOES FROM THE FLESH OF AN ANIMAL SACRED TO MY PEOPLE.

TOUCHÉ.

KWIKE BEEF

SHOPPING AT YOUR STORE HAS GIVEN ME AN IDEA FOR MY NEXT SERMON.

THANK YOU, COME AGAIN!

THAT SUNDAY...

First Church of Springfield
Christmas Sermon! Welcome Once A Year Congregants!

I'D LIKE TO START THIS YEAR'S CHRISTMAS SERMON WITH A SAD CONFESSION.

OH, DEAR!

HE'S GONNA 'FESS UP TO HAVING A TASTE FOR COMMUNION WINE, ISN'T HE?

I MUST CONFESS THAT I AM DISAPPOINTED. CHRISTMAS HAS BECOME SO COMMERCIALIZED THAT I BELIEVE ITS MEANING IS *LOST* ON YOU.

DADDY, HAVE *YOU* LOST IT?

NO. *I* HAVEN'T!

YOU PEOPLE MARGINALIZE CHRISTMAS MORE AND MORE, EVERY YEAR. YOU PUT MORE EMPHASIS UPON CHESTNUT ROASTING, EGG NOGGING, AND GIFT WRAPPING THAN WHAT THE DAY IS REALLY ABOUT.

PARDON THE INTERRUPTION, BUT DON'T YOU THINK YOU'RE BEING A TAD HARSH ON THE GOOD OL' FLOCK?

DON'T TAKE MY WORD FOR IT. HEAR IT FROM THE MOUTH OF BABES!

BART SIMPSON, WHAT DOES CHRISTMAS MEAN TO YOU?

HUH?

IT MEANS I'M GETTIN' THE NEW *"GRAND THEFT SKATEBOARD"* GAME FOR MY X-STATION!

LISA, CAN *YOU* TELL US ABOUT CHRISTMAS?

SURE. IT ACTUALLY EVOLVED FROM THE ROMAN PAGAN FESTIVAL 'DIES NATALIS SOLIS INVICTI.' THE WINTER SOLSTICE...

THANK YOU. THAT'S ENOUGH!

FINALLY, LET'S TRY RALPH WIGGUM.

CHRISTMAS IS A BIRTHDAY PARTY!

GOOD! WHO'S BIRTHDAY?

SANTA'S!

≥SIGH≤ I GUESS HE'S RIGHT.

CHRISTMAS IS *NOT* "X-MAS." CHRISTMAS IS *NOT* ABOUT CANDY CANES OR MISTLETOE. IT'S *NOT* ABOUT DUFF'S SEASONAL *JINGLE BREW!*

MMM...I FORGOT THAT'S HIT THE SHELVES BY NOW!

I CHALLENGE YOU ALL TO REMEMBER WHY WE CELEBRATE EVERY DECEMBER. HERE'S A HINT. IT'S *NOT* SANTA! *SANTA CLAUS DOES NOT EXIST!*

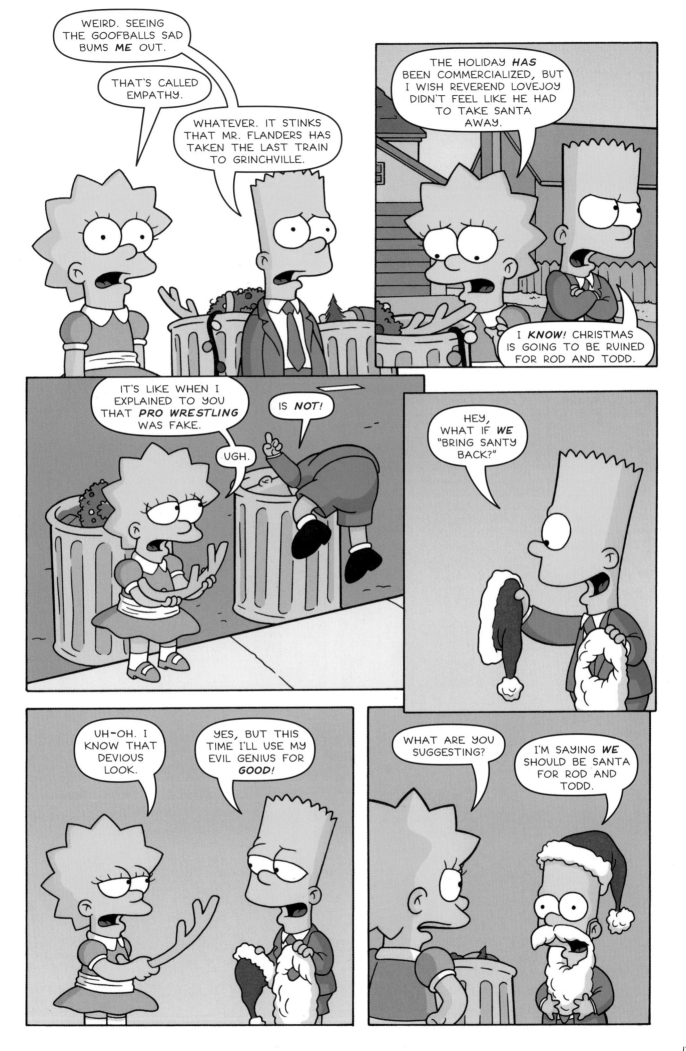

CHRISTMAS EVE—OPERATION PAPA NOEL.

PLUNK!

CHING! CHING! CHING!

SANTA IS COMING! HE'S WORKING HIS WAY DOWN THE STREET!

SLEIGH BELLS RING! ARE YOU LISTENING?

I DO HEAR SLEIGH BELLS!

SANTA'S SLEIGH!

LOOK OVER THERE!

WE BETTER GO PUT OUT THE MILK AND COOKIES!

GOOD JOB, BART. THEY BOUGHT IT!

THANKS, BUT I'M NOT SURE HOW I'M GETTING THE DOG OFF THE ROOF.

I KNOW THIS WAS MY PLAN, BUT DO I HAVE TO WEAR DAD'S OLD SANTA SUIT JUST TO BITE A COOKIE?

YES! IF THE BOYS SNEAK A PEEK, YOU NEED TO LOOK LIKE SANTA!

THE COSTUME IS A LITTLE BIG ON YOU.

IT'S NOT THE SIZE THAT'S KILLING ME. IT'S THE STINK! I DON'T THINK HOMER EVER WASHED IT AFTER HIS SANTA JOB AT THE SPRINGFIELD MALL. IT REEKS OF STALE BEER AND THE TODDLER DIAPERS THAT SAT ON HIS LAP.

HEY, KIDS! WHAT ARE YOU UP TO?

UH, NOTHING...

JUST SPREADING A LITTLE HOLIDAY CHEER.

AW, THAT'S NICE.

WE'VE BEEN GETTING REPORTS OF *A PROWLER* IN YOUR NEIGHBORHOOD, SO BE CAREFUL!

NO PROBLEM-O!

MERRY CHRISTMAS!

THAT WAS CLOSE. WE BETTER NOT WASTE ANY-MORE TIME.

HOLD ON. THE BOYS HAVE TO DO *THEIR* PART.

DADDY THREW OUT ALL THE CHRISTMAS COOKIE CUTTERS, SO I HOPE SANTA LIKES SNICKER-DOODLES!

WE NEED TO TUCK BACK IN BEFORE SANTA GETS HERE!

OKAY, THEY'RE GONE.

LET'S JUST HOPE MR. FLANDERS DOESN'T HAVE A *HO-HO-HOME* SECURITY SYSTEM.

ONE GOOD CHOMP ON THIS COOKIE AND ROD AND TODD WILL KNOW THAT SANTA WAS HERE.

CREAK!

WHAT THE--?! SANTA *IS* HERE!

BART SIMPSON!

SNAKE! YOU'RE BREAKING INTO HOUSES DRESSED AS SANTA ON CHRISTMAS EVE? THAT'S *LOW!*

OH, YEAH? WHY ARE *YOU* SNEAKING AROUND IN YOUR NEIGHBOR'S HOUSE DRESSED LIKE JOLLY OLD ST. NICK?

WELL...

18

DADDY DOESN'T NEED TO POP A CA-DIDDLY-AP IN KRIS KRINGLE'S KEISTER. ONE CALL TO THE POLICE AND THEY'LL TAKE THIS *BAD SANTA* TO THE NORTH POLE PENITENTIARY.

WAIT!

LISA? BART?

MR. FLANDERS, I AGREE THAT TOO MANY HOLIDAY ADS LIKE "MERRY SQUISHMAS" HAVE CLOUDED THE *TRUE MEANING* OF CHRISTMAS.

I KINDA *LIKE* THE PINEY FLAVOR OF THE X-MAS GREEN SQUISHEE.

DO YOU DOUBT THAT YOUR SONS KNOW THE *SPIRITUAL SIGNIFICANCE OF CHRISTMAS?*

WELL...NO. I *KNOW* THEY KNOW.

EVEN THOUGH CHRISTMAS IS A CHRISTIAN HOLIDAY, IT IS OBSERVED BY MANY NON-CHRISTIANS. IT'S A SEASON WHEN PEOPLE TRY A LITTLE HARDER TO BE GOOD TO ONE ANOTHER. SANTA IS A *SYMBOL* OF THAT.

THE WARMTH AND GOODWILL OF CHRISTMAS TIME BRINGS OUT THE BEST IN PEOPLE.

SURE, THE "RED AND WHITE" VERSION THAT WE'RE FAMILIAR WITH TODAY WAS MANUFACTURED BY A COLA COMPANY, BUT THAT DOESN'T CHANGE THE FACT THAT SANTA IS A SYMBOL OF *PEACE* AND *JOY*.

DON'T TAKE THE JOY AWAY FROM ROD AND TODD.

WELL, GOSH AND GOLLY. WHEN YOU PUT IT LIKE THAT, I GUESS I CAN LET SANTA OFF WITH A WARNING.

YAY!

THANKS, DADDY!

I THINK IT'S TIME FOR SANTA TO LEAVE THAT BAG OF GIFTS, GET BACK TO HIS SLEIGH, AND HIT THE ROAD.

THE END

21

CONVERSATION STARTERS

THE FOLLOWING ARE EXAMPLES OF SURE-FIRE CONVERSATIONAL OPENERS. THESE GREGARIOUS LITTLE GEMS ARE PERFECT FOR BREAKING THE ICE AT PARTIES AND ARE GUARANTEED TO TURN EVEN THE DULLEST ROUND OF CHITTER-CHATTER INTO A CONFABULOUS GABFEST.

BART'S LIST OF TRULY UNSPEAKABLE WORDS AND PHRASES

HEH, HEH, HEH!

THINGS TO DO

1	2	3	4	5	6	7
8	9	10	11	12	13	14
15 DRIVE HOMER CRAZY	16 MESS WITH HOMER'S MIND	17 CAUSE HOMER TO BLOW HIS STACK	18 DESTROY HOMER'S SENSE OF WELL-BEING	19 GIVE HOMER A MENTAL MELT-DOWN	20 GET HOMER TO FLIP OUT	21 MAKE HOMER HAVE A COW, MAN
23	24	25	26	27	28	29
30	31					

SCOTT SHAW! SCRIPT	JOHN COSTANZA PENCILS	PHYLLIS NOVIN INKS	ROBERT STANLEY COLORS	KAREN BATES LETTERS	BILL MORRISON EDITOR

IT'S BEEN QUITE A *WEEK* AROUND THE *SIMPSONS HOME!* LET'S START WITH LAST *SUNDAY*...

YEOWTCH!

BART!

Y'KNOW, THERE'S *NOTHING* AS MUCH *FUN* AS USING A PNEUMATIC *STAPLE GUN* TO PLAY *TARGET PRACTICE* WITH YOUR SISTER'S COLLECTION OF *HAPPY LITTLE ELVES* FIGURES!

SPLUTT!

CHUNK!

MATT GROENING

MONDAY...

C'MON, MILHOUSE! THIS CAN GET US *EXTRA CREDIT* FOR MRS. KRABAPPEL'S UNIT ON *EDGAR ALLEN POE!*

UH, I DUNNO, BART! I'M *TOO YOUNG* TO BE SEALED INSIDE A *WALL* WITH A *CASK* OF SPANISH *WINE!*

TOO LATE! I'M *ALREADY* WHIPPING UP A FRESH BATCH OF *CONCRETE!*

BART!

BUT LATER THAT EVENING, HOMER DECIDES TO GIVE "BRAINFOOD" A CHANCE...

HEY, YOU NEVER KNOW...THIS MAG MIGHT HAVE SOME CARTOONS IN IT!

WOW, I'VE NEVER SEEN SO MANY ADVERTISEMENTS FOR SCENTED ROOM FRESHENERS!

FLIP! FLIP! FLIP! FLIP!

BRAINFOOD

SO WHAT'S THIS ARTICLE?

Is your young child 'ACTING OUT?'

It's absolutely necessary not to acknowledge his increasingly wild stunts, which are primarily intended to attract your attention!

WELL, THAT MAKES NO SENSE...I'VE HAD IT WITH "BRAINFOOD"! IT'S ABOUT AS IN TOUCH WITH REALITY AS AN ISSUE OF RADIOACTIVE MAN COMICS!

CLICK!

BRAINFOOD

INSTEAD, LET'S TAKE A LOOK AT WHAT'S ON THE GOOD OL' DEPENDABLE TV, SHALL WE?

THIS IS KENT BROCKMAN WITH A SPECIAL REPORT FROM STATE PRISON, WHERE YOUNG LAWBREAKERS GET A STARTLING DOSE OF LIFE BEHIND BARS!

OOOH, IT'S ONE OF THOSE "SCARED STRAIGHT" PROGRAMS!

I JUST LOVE SEEING YOUNG HOODLUMS GET INTIMIDATED BY HARDENED PRISON INMATES!

ALTHOUGH THE YOUNGSTERS HAVEN'T ACTUALLY BEEN ARRESTED, "OPERATION: TOUGH LOVE" INTENDS TO DISCOURAGE THEM FROM FOLLOWING A LIFE OF CRIME!

THIS IS WAY MORE ENTERTAINING THAN MARGE'S STUPID OL' MAGAZINE!

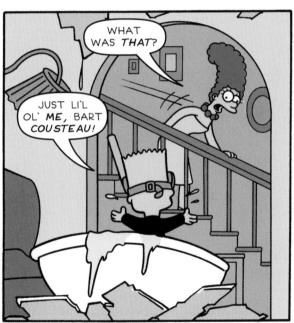

ALL RIGHT, INMATE SIMPSON... MEET YOUR NEW CELLMATE... *SHIV!*

HEY, *I* KNOW *YOU...* YOU'RE THE DUDE WHO HANGS OUT BY THE *DUMPSTERS* BEHIND THE *KWIK-E-MART!*

PUT 'ER *THERE,* MAN!

HEY, DUDE!

BUMP!

Y'KNOW, I REALLY *DIG* MEETING THE *NEW GENERATION* OF *CRIMINAL-TYPES!*

THEY'RE ALWAYS SO *REFRESHING!*

YOU *KNOW* IT, MAN... REFRESHINGLY *AWESOME!*

EARLY THE NEXT MORNING...

DUDES, I WANT YOU TO MEET *BART,* MY NEW *CELLMATE!* HE MAY BE KINDA *YOUNG,* BUT HE'S *ALL RIGHT!*

WHAT ARE YOU *IN* FOR, MAN?

ER...DROPPING A *BATHTUB* FULL OF *WATER* ON MY *OLD MAN...*I GUESS!

WHOA! ARE *YOU* EVER *HARDCORE!*

I AM?

OH, YEAH! THE WORST *I* EVER HEARD ABOUT WAS A DUDE WHO DROPPED A *CAGE* FULL OF BLOOD-THIRSTY *LIVE LOBSTERS* ON HIS OLD MAN!

HEY! THAT WAS *ME,* TOO!

YEAH, I GUESS I *AM* PRETTY *HARDCORE* AT THAT!

WITH A *REPUTATION* LIKE HIS, IT DOESN'T TAKE BART *LONG* TO ASCEND TO THE *TOP* OF THE PENAL *HEAP*...

OKAY, SAY YOU'VE GOT A *MIRROR*, A *MARBLE*, AND A *GARDEN HOSE*...WHAT WOULD YOU *MAKE* OUT OF 'EM?

WELL, FOR STARTERS, HOW 'BOUT A *GIANT SLINGSHOT* WITH A MULTI-DIRECTIONAL *TARGETING DEVICE*?

WHY DIDN'T *I* THINK OF THAT?

SHHH! QUIET, MCGUYVER!

"THE USE OF OBJECTS FOUND IN A CONFINED SPACE -- CREATIVE PRACTICAL JOKERY" INSTRUCTOR: BART SIMPSON

ALL RIGHT, SO WE ALL *AGREE* THAT *FLATULANT NOISES* ARE *100%* RELIABLY *FUNNY AND EMBARRASSING*...

...ALLOW ME TO *DEMONSTRATE* HOW TO USE *VENTRILOQUISM* TO SEND YOUR ENEMIES AROUND A CORNER AND RIGHT INTO CHIEF WIGGUM'S *OFFICE*... WHILE HE'S MEETING WITH THE *POLICE COMMISSIONER*!

BRILLIANT! BUT WHAT IF CHIEF WIGGUM MAKES SOME OF HIS *OWN* "FUNNY AND EMBARRASSING" *GASSY SOUNDS* BEFORE *YOU* DO?

"ADVANCED DISSING OF AUTHORITY"

INSTRUCTOR: BART SIMPSON

SO, IF THIS *SLOPPY JOE* REPRESENTS A *GUARD*, THE *CREAMED CORN* REPRESENTS YOUR *BUDDY*, THE *LIMA BEANS* REPRESENT A *TOTAL SOLAR ECLIPSE*, AND THE *TAPIOCA PUDDING* REPRESENTS *YOU*...

WHO CARES? YOU *GRAB* THE STUFF, *WHIP* IT AT SOME-ONE'S HEAD...

...AND START YOURSELF A *FOOD FIGHT*!

WHERE HAS THIS KID *BEEN* ALL OUR LIVES?

SEMINAR: IMPROVISATIONAL TROUBLEMAKING 101 INSTRUCTOR: BART SIMPSON

SPLATT!

WITHIN A FEW HOURS, THE *POLICE STATION* AND ITS *JAILHOUSE* FIND THEMSELVES *OVER-WHELMED* BY A WAVE OF *GONZO MAYHEM*...

SPREAD OUT, BOYS, BEFORE THESE *RIOTERS* GET THE *UPPER HAND!*

DON'T LOOK *NOW,* CHIEF, BUT I THINK THEY'VE *ALREADY* GOT THE UPPER HAND!

HECK, IF YOU ASK *ME,* THEY'VE GOT THE ENTIRE *FORE-ARM!*

I DON'T KNOW WHAT'S GOING ON, BUT I'M HERE TO SIGN UP AS A *POLLING PLACE VOLUNTEER*...

ALL *RIIIGHT!* NOW *THAT'S* WHAT I CALL *"IMPROVISATIONAL TROUBLEMAKING"*

C'MON, DUDES, LET'S MAKE LI'L BART *PROUD!*

AHHH...I SEE THAT MY *STUDENTS* HAVE *LEARNED* THEIR *LESSONS* QUITE *WELL,* INDEED!

Y'KNOW, THOSE *SEMINARS* WERE GOOD FOR *ME,* TOO... KINDA GOT ME TO *EXAMINE* AND *REFINE* MY *THINKING!*

I'M GONNA HAVE TO *THANK* HOMER FOR PUTTING ME *THROUGH* SUCH AN *ENRICHING EXPERIENCE!*

UHHH...I'M NOT *ALONE* HERE, AM I?

ABSOLUTELY HAW-HAW-LARIOUS
JOY BUZZER

THIS "SHOCKING" GAG IS A SURE-FIRE RIB TICKLER!

COMPLETELY HARMLESS, UNFORTUNATELY.

ONLY $2

Consult your attorney before using.

SO FUNNY YOU'LL FORGET TO LAUGH!
STINK BOMB

A MEASLY $2

Offer void in Alabama, Alaska, Arizona, Arkansas, California, Colorado, Connecticut, Delaware, Florida, Georgia, Hawaii, Idaho, Illinois, Indiana, Iowa, Kansas, Kentucky, Louisiana, Maine, Maryland, Massachusetts, Michigan, Minnesota, Mississippi, Missouri, Montana, Nebraska, Nevada, New Hampshire, New Jersey, New Mexico, New York, North Carolina, North Dakota, Ohio, Oklahoma, Oregon, Pennsylvania, Rhode Island, South Carolina, South Dakota, Tennessee, Utah, Vermont, Virginia, Washington, West Virginia, Wisconsin and Wyoming.

EWWW! WHAT DID THAT
DOGGIE DOO?

OUR FAKE DOG POO IS SO REALISTIC, EVEN YOUR DOG WON'T KNOW WHODUNIT!

JUST A TRIFLING $3

AMAZING! X-Ray Glasses

AN INFINITESIMAL $3

X-SPEXTRA® IS THE LATEST SPACE AGE SCIENTIFIC OPTICAL DISCOVERY THAT GIVES YOU THE POWER TO "SEE" THROUGH WALLS AND LADIES OUTER GARMENTS!

You'll have loads of fun when you put these on and "see" that the joke's on you!

OUR COMPLETE CATALOG OF OVER 1,000
PRANK PHONE CALL NAMES

Including such all-time favorites as:

Amanda Huggenkiss

Jacques Strap

Seymour Butz

Ivana Tinkle

Anita Bath

Maya Normousbutt

A MERE $2

GET BILLED BY THE MINUTE FOR HOURS OF FUN!

COUPON:

Ye Olde Gagge Shoppe
Yuk-ingham Palace

P.O. Box 42 Springfield, USA

RUSH me the following laff-a-minute, crowd-pleasing gag items:

_____

_____

I will be using these novelty items mainly to:

☐ Avenge myself   ☐ Annoy others

☐ Get attention   ☐ Spread laughter and joy

Name _____

Address _____

A GUY'S GUIDE TO GOING OUT WITH GALS

UNLUCKY IN LOVE?
WELL, IF YOU'RE LIKE ME,
YOU BLAME YOURSELF, BUT LET'S FACE IT,
GIRLS SEND OUT MORE MIXED SIGNALS THAN
A SEMAPHORE FLAG WAVER WITH HEAD LICE. THAT'S
WHY I'M OFFERING UP THESE SURE-FIRE TIPS
FOR NAVIGATING THE TEMPESTUOUS
SEA OF LOVE.

DATING DON'Ts & DOs

DON'T

- Be yourself. Imagine the kind of guy that a girl would go on a second date with and then pretend to be that guy.

- Relax and have a good time. This will only lead to you doing or saying or being something stupid.

- Have anything to eat or drink. Food is messy and liquids make you squirmy.

- Be considerate. Chicks love bad boys. At least that's what I read in Cosmo.

- Be too picky. Remember, if a girl accepts a date with you, her standards aren't very high either.

- Let her out of your sight for a minute. She's liable to make a break for it and run home.

- Call her the next day. She may have already forgotten who you are. Call her the minute you get home from your date.

DO

Everything on the "don't" list.

ASK MILHOUSE

Q: Are there some things men are simply expected to do for women?
M: Oh, boy! Are there ever! Whoa! I'll say! Don't get me started! Oh, man!

Q: What are some of these things?
M: I have no idea.

Q: What is the proper way for a boy to ask a girl for a date?
M: Please? Please? *Pleeeeeeeeeeeease?*

THE PATENTED VAN HOUTEN DATE ASKER DE-HUMILIATOR

IN MY COPIOUS SPARE TIME, I HAVE DEVELOPED A TECHNIQUE FOR ASKING FOR A DATE THAT HAS THE YOUNG LADY'S REFUSAL BUILT RIGHT INTO THE PROPOSAL. THIS WAY, A GIRL CAN'T TURN ME DOWN WITHOUT SAYING "YES"!

DO YOU WANT TO GO THE MOVIES WITH ME ON SATURDAY, OR DO YOU HAVE TO WASH THE CAT?

YES, I DO.

CAN I WALK YOU HOME, OR DO YOU PREFER TO USE PUBLIC TRANSPORTATION AND SPEND 40 MINUTES SITTING IN THE HOT SUN ON A FILTHY BENCH WAITING FOR THE CROSSTOWN BUS?

OH, YES. ANYTIME.

WILL YOU LET ME CALL ON YOU TOMORROW NIGHT, OR WILL YOU BE HAVING YOUR APPENDIX REMOVED *AGAIN*?

YES, I WILL.

MAY I TAKE YOU TO THE SPRING DANCE NEXT WEEK, OR WOULD YOU JUST AS SOON STAY HOME ALL ALONE AND GO STARK RAVING MAD STARING AT THE WALLPAPER?

GOSH, YES. THAT'S SOUNDS *GREAT!*

HOW ABOUT LUNCH SOME AFTERNOON, OR WOULD YOU RATHER DIE AND ROT IN HELL FIRST?

YES, WE WOULD! THANK YOU VERY MUCH. SOUNDS GREAT!

38

NOT A (GREEN, SLIMY) CREATURE WAS STIRRING

ARIE KAPLAN
SCRIPT

PHIL ORTIZ
PENCILS

MIKE DECARLO
INKS

NATHAN HAMILL
COLORS

KAREN BATES
LETTERS

BILL MORRISON
EDITOR

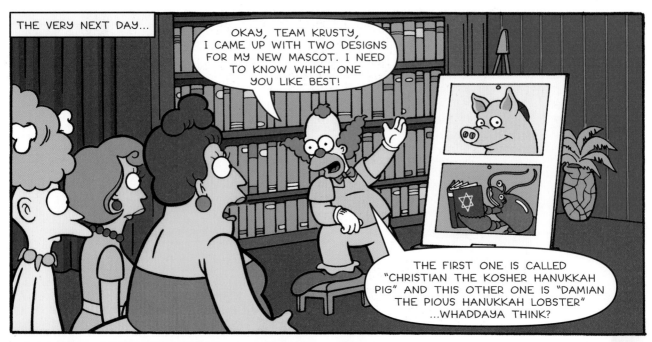

THE VERY NEXT DAY...

OKAY, TEAM KRUSTY, I CAME UP WITH TWO DESIGNS FOR MY NEW MASCOT. I NEED TO KNOW WHICH ONE YOU LIKE BEST!

THE FIRST ONE IS CALLED "CHRISTIAN THE KOSHER HANUKKAH PIG" AND THIS OTHER ONE IS "DAMIAN THE PIOUS HANUKKAH LOBSTER" ...WHADDAYA THINK?

COME ON, YES-MEN! GET TO YESSING! WHY AREN'T YOU TELLING ME HOW GREAT MY IDEAS ARE?

KRUSTY, YOUR DRAWINGS... STIR UP EMOTIONS I DIDN'T KNOW I HAD. BUT THEY, UH...LACK SOMETHING...

IS IT SHRIMP? BECAUSE I GOT ANOTHER ONE, "SHLOMO THE HANUKKAH SHRIMP."

NO, THEY LACK...ER, A CHILD'S TOUCH!

A CHILD'S TOUCH, EH?

HEY, I GOT IT! I'LL BRING IN SOME ACTUAL CHILDREN TO DESIGN THE MASCOT FOR ME!

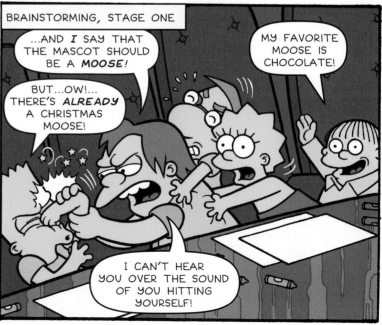

BRAINSTORMING, STAGE TWO

WHY DON'T WE MAKE THE MASCOT A MANTA RAY?

OR A PEGASUS?

OR A STAPLER?

I SAY WE MAKE THE MASCOT A TURTLE.

TURTLES? EWW! WE JUST READ ABOUT THEM IN SCIENCE CLASS. THEY MOULT THEIR DEAD SKIN! IT LOOKS LIKE THIN SHEETS OF PLASTIC, BUT IT'S REALLY :SHUDDER: PIECES OF *TURTLE*!

COOL!

GENTLEMEN, I REST MY CASE.

BRAINSTORMING, STAGE THREE

NO, BART, WE CAN'T CALL HIM "POOPFACE, THE POOPING TURTLE THAT POOPS EVERYWHERE AND SMELLS HIS OWN POOP."

STUPID FCC REGULATIONS.

THE TURTLE'S FLIPPERS HAVE *THREE* FINGERS, AND MY FLIPPERS HAVE *FOUR* FINGERS!

RALPH, *THAT'S IT!*

47

THE END

LISA'S LIST OF UTTERLY REPREHENSIBLE WORDS AND PHRASES

Q: What are the basic rules of etiquette?

H: Sit down and shut up.

Q: How important is the use of courteous words and phrases, such as "Excuse me," "Please," and "Thank you"?

H: Oh, those work great when you're shoving your way through a crowded theatre or shopping mall: "Excuse me, please. Thank you!"… "Excuse me, please. Thank you!" and so forth.

Q: Does the use of polite words sometime merely mask rude actions?

H: Exactly. That's what good breeding is all about.

Q: At a party, what are the guests' responsibilities?

H: Guests have no responsibilities. That's what makes it a party. You show up, you eat, you insult your hostess, you embarrass your wife, you throw up on the front lawn, you go home. That's really all there is to being a guest. If you're gonna go around giving guests responsibilities, no one is ever gonna show up at your stupid parties.

Q: How does one instill good manners in one's children?

H: I generally like to start with an insult and some name-calling.

Q: What is meant by the old adage, "Children should be seen and not heard"?

H: Oooh, that's creepy! Imagine them crawling all over the house, not making a sound, just staring at you with those big eyes. Eeeeww!

Q: Is it ever acceptable to discipline one's child in public?

H: Did you say one's child or just one child? Because if you mean just one, then I'm gonna have to choose the boy.

CONVERSATION STOPPERS

THE FOLLOWING ARE EXAMPLES OF RHETORICAL QUESTIONS, THAT IS, A QUESTION ASKED MERELY FOR EFFECT WITH NO ANSWER EXPECTED. WHEN CONFRONTED WITH QUESTIONS SUCH AS THESE, DO NOT, UNDER ANY CIRCUMSTANCES, ATTEMPT AN ANSWER!

53

54 TONY DIGEROLAMO CARLOS VALENTI STEVE STEERE, JR. ROBERT STANLEY KAREN BATES BILL MORRISON
SCRIPT PENCILS INKS COLORS LETTERS EDITOR

THE END

TONY DIGEROLAMO
SCRIPT

CARLOS VALENTI
PENCILS

STEVE STEERE, JR.
INKS

ROBERT STANLEY
COLORS

KAREN BATES
LETTERS

BILL MORRISON
EDITOR

HEY, DUDE! THIS TIGHT HILL HAS LIKE A TOTAL BULLET-PROOF S-RAIL COMING UP. BETTER DUCKFOOT THAT PHAT BOARD OR YOU'LL BE DOING A SICK FAKIE HIP!

WICKED!

AHHHH!!!

OH. GUESS THAT PART WAS THE SAME. BUT AT LEAST HE UNDERSTOOD WHAT THE OTHER DUDE SAID!

AND NOW *YOU* CAN UNDERSTAND BY USING THIS HANDY SNOWBOARDER'S TRANSLATOR!

SNOWBOARDER	ENGLISH
THAT HILL SHREDS.	THAT HILL WILL PROBABLY BREAK SOMEBODY'S COLLARBONE.
WHOA, DUDE! YOU'RE HARSHIN' MY BUZZ!	MY ENTHUSIASM WANES AS YOU SPEAK TO ME.
BOARDERS RULE! SKIERS DROOL!	I PREFER TO SNOWBOARD. SKIING IS DÉCLASSÉ.
MAN, I TOTALLY SURFED THAT 'LANCHE!	I WAS NEARLY KILLED BY AN AVALANCHE TODAY!
BOGUS! MY DEW'S BEEN BREACHED.	GRACIOUS! SOMEONE DRANK MY SODA.
I HAVE TO BLAST A DOOKIE.	I HAVE TO GO TO THE BATHROOM.
WOW, THAT CHICK DID A TIGHT! WHO IS SHE?	I AM ENAMORED BY THAT WOMAN'S SNOW-RODEO. PERHAPS I WILL TALK TO HER.
DUDE! CHECK IT!	PAY ATTENTION TO ME GOOD FRIEND, FOR I AM AN EXPERT SNOWBOARDER, AND IF YOU DON'T LOOK, MY AMAZING TRICK WILL BE HISTORY, JUST LIKE SANDS THROUGH AN HOURGLASS LOST IN THE WINDS OF TIME.

HIBERNATIN' HOMER

PAUL DINI & MISTY LEE
SCRIPT

JAMES LLOYD
PENCILS

ANDREW PEPOY
INKS

NATHAN HAMILL
COLORS

KAREN BATES
LETTERS

BILL MORRISON
EDITOR

ARE YOU SURE THIS IS SAFE, PROFESSOR?

OH, NO NEED TO WORRY. HOMER IS THE PERFECT GUINEA PIG FOR MY NEW MAXIMUM STRENGTH SEDATIVE.

AWW! I DON'T WANNA SLEEP LIKE A GUINEA PIG, I WANNA SLEEP LIKE A *BEAR!*

AND SO YOU SHALL, MY CORPULENT FRIEND.

ONE SIP OF THIS BREW AND YOU'LL BE OUT UNTIL EASTER, WITH THE BUNNIES AND CHICKIES AND THE MARSHMALLOW PEEPS ⋮GA-HOY!⋮

NOTHIN'.

⋮ZZAAWW!⋮

WHEN HOMER EMERGES FROM HIS HIBERNATION, HE WILL BE RESTED, REFRESHED, AND A GOOD HUNDRED POUNDS LIGHTER!

SLEEP TIGHT, HOMIE!

THAT SOLVES DAD'S PROBLEM. NOW HOW ARE *WE* GOING TO SURVIVE WINTER WHILE OUR BREADWINNER IS SLEEPING OFF HIS FLAB?

IT SHOULDN'T BE TOO HARD IF WE ALL PITCH IN.

MEANWHILE, BACK AT THE SNOOZE-CAVE...

ZZZAAWWW...

IN HERE, GENTS...

WE WILL STASH THE GOODS IN THIS OUT OF THE WAY CAVE UNTIL SAINT VALENTINE'S DAY.

BRILLIANT SCHEME, BOSS. HIJACKING ALL THE CONVERSATION HEART SHIPMENTS INTO SPRINGFIELD.

THANK YOU, LEGS. THE LOVEBIRDS WILL HAVE TO PAY DEARLY THIS YEAR IF THEY WANT THEIR "OH U KID."

ZZZAWWW...

HEY, WE GOT A SPY!

YOU WANT I SHOULD WASTE SLEEPING UGLY?

NOT SO FAST, LOUIE. THERE IS SOMETHING FAMILIAR ABOUT HIM.

I BELIEVE THIS IS NONE OTHER THAN MY OLD ASSOCIATE IN CRIME, AUGIE "SLEEPY" MANETTI!

THE LEGENDARY SNOOZING HITMAN OF HACKENSACK?!

WE ARE IN THE PRESENCE OF GREATNESS!

NO DOUBT SLEEPY WAS HIDING OUT AFTER A BUSY MONTH OF HOLIDAY WHACKINGS. PERHAPS WE CAN PERSUADE HIM TO JOIN OUR MERRY BAND UNTIL THE SPRING THAW.

ZZAAWWW...

THAT SOUNDS LIKE A "YES" TO ME.

FIX HIM UP NICELY, MARIO. NOTHING IS TOO GOOD FOR SLEEPY MANETTI.

ZZZZ...

SI, SI, FAT TONY.

WELL, HERMAN, I SEE THAT YOU ARE STILL A FEW HUNDRED DOLLARS SHORT ON THOSE AUTHENTIC SICILIAN GARROTES WE OBTAINED FOR YOU.

SORRY, TONY. YOU KNOW HOW IT IS...NO ONE'S SPENDING MONEY AFTER NEW YEAR'S. IF I COULD HAVE ANOTHER COUPLE WEEKS...

I SYMPATHIZE, HERMAN, BUT BUSINESS IS BUSINESS. SLEEPY, LEAN ON HIM.

ZZZZ...

ZZZZ...

OW! I'LL PAY! I'LL PAY!

TO SLEEPY MANETTI! IN THE MONTH SINCE YOU JOINED US, NOT A PAYMENT HAS BEEN MISSED, NOT A DEADBEAT HAS GONE UNFLATTENED!

ZZZ...

TO SLEEPY!

IT CREEPS ME OUT THE WAY HE CAN EAT AND SLEEP LIKE THAT.

THE MAN IS AN ARTIST AT WHAT HE DOES. DO NOT CRITICIZE.

FREEZE, SLEAZE!

FAITH AND BEGORRAH! 'TIS THAT LOVABLE LUSH-PRECHAUN, TIPPLE O'TOOLE, HERE TO BRING YOU DUFF'S NEWEST BREW, SHAMROCK SUDS!

THIS MARCH, JOIN TIPPLE ON HIS CHUG-DOWN TO ST. PADDY'S DAY! YOU CAN CATCH HIM AT THE SPRINGFIELD MONSTER TRUCK RALLY...

THE BEER 'N' BRAWL'S SPRING T-SHIRT SPRAY...

...OR YOUR LOCAL DIVE OF CHOICE! BUT CATCH HIM QUICK, BECAUSE THE FUN ENDS MARCH 18TH!

OUT, RUMMIES! SEE YOU ON CINCO DE MAYO!

IF I NEVER SEE GREEN FOAM AGAIN, IT WILL BE TOO SOON!

AMEN!

ZZZ... ¿GURGLE...¿

DUFF'S SHAMROCK SUDS WERE A RUNAWAY SUCCESS. WE OWE IT ALL TO YOU, TIPPLE.

BUT WHAT DO WE DO WITH HIM NOW THAT THE PROMOTION IS OVER?

SPRINGFIELD HOLIDAY CHARACTER TEMP AGENCY...OH HELLO, MRS. QUIMBY...A BIG, FAT JOLLY EASTER BUNNY FOR THE MAYOR'S ANNUAL EASTER EGG ROLL? I'M SORRY, BUT...

THE SPRINGFIELD HOLIDAY CHARACTER TEMP AGENCY

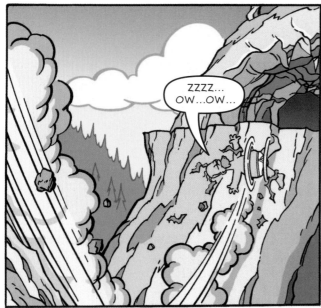

HAVE A BLAST
WITH THESE GREAT SIMPSONS BOOKS!
www.titanbooks.com

ISBN: 9781852865979

ISBN: 9781852866693

ISBN: 9781852867270

ISBN: 9781852867645

ISBN: 9781852868062

ISBN: 9781852869557

ISBN: 9781840230581

ISBN: 9781840231519

ISBN: 9781840234039

ISBN: 9781840235920

ISBN: 9781840237900

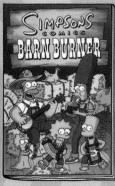

ISBN: 9781845760106

ISBN: 9781845762285

ISBN: 9781845764104

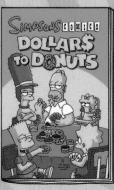

ISBN: 9781845767518

ISBN: 9781848562271

ISBN: 9781852868208

ISBN: 9781840234251

ISBN: 9781840236545

ISBN: 9781840238464

ISBN: 9781845760571

ISBN: 9781845763046

ISBN: 9781845764111

ISBN: 9781845767525

ISBN: 9781848562288

FEED YOUR NEED FOR COMEDY WITH SIMPSONS COMICS!

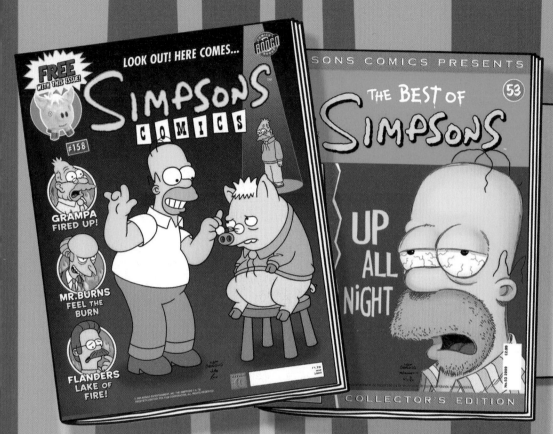

ON SALE EVERY 4 WEEKS AND WITH A GREAT FREE GIFT TOO!

AND IF YOU LIKE SIMPSONS, YOU'LL LOVE OUR FUTURAMA COMICS!

Titan Comics

ORDER NOW ☎ 0844 844 0248
www.titancomicsuk.com